BACK TO YOU

It's Personal Again

SET IN SOUL

THIS JOURNAL BELONGS TO

_____

DEDICATED TO THOSE WHO REFUSE TO
GIVE UP ON LOVE

TABLE OF CONTENTS

HOW TO USE THIS JOURNAL

Every thought. Every emotion. Every feeling. Write it here. In your journal. This is your place where you are free to express your truth about what happened and what you want for yourself moving forward. Writing in your own words the thoughts you couldn't express to others breaks through layers of hurt and pain that triggers unwanted behavior. Seeing your words written out not only provides a sense of release but also starts a creation of new life for you. Because your Words create, and this is your time to not only let go of your past, but also to create a new future - a new love life that first starts with loving yourself.

This journal will guide you through three different stages towards healing. The first sixty days will help you identify what you need, not just from future relationships, but also from yourself. It is in this process that you will begin to let go of what you thought you were receiving and start providing it to yourself. It is in this stage that you will begin to let go of pain, false promises and the security you thought you had. You will begin to feel light again as you decide that it is time for a change.

This is stage two. During the next sixty days, you will start to identify what really needs to change within you and around you. You will notice that the factors you use to make decisions have changed. You will become aware of beliefs that you held that no longer serve you and replace them with those that cause you to be stronger and live a life filled with love, passion and expectation. It is through these new beliefs you will start to get back to the core of who you are and stand firm to what you are willing to receive.

This is stage three. The last sixty days of this journal will lead you to become whatever you want. This means moving forward with what you will and will not allow into your space. This is the time to declare what is for you. This is your time internally welcome in all the moments that belong to you. You will be open for true love again and it will be time to paint that picture of what it will look and feel like because you will receive it.

This is a time where it comes back to you. It's now personal again.

It's not a coincidence that you have this journal. It was created for you.

WHAT WENT WRONG?

What Caused Your Relationship To End?

Are You Happy That It Ended?

Who Do You Blame For The Break Up?

Did You And Your Previous Partner Try To Work On Your Problems?

When Did You Or Your Previous Partner Stop Trying To Work On The Relationship?

What Made You Stop Fighting For Your Relationship?

Did Your Previous Partner Respect You?

Did You Trust Your Previous Partner?

Did Your Partner Help You To Grow Mentally And/Or Spiritually?

Did You Put Your Previous Partner's Needs Before Your Own?

What Are Your Complaints About Your Previous Partner?

What Did Your Previous Partner Complain About When It Came To You?

What Did You Learn From Your Relationship?

If You Can Say One Last Thing To Your Ex, What Would It Be?

SECTION ONE:

WHAT DO I NEED?

WHAT DO I NEED?

Date:

Today I Want God To Know:

I'm Happy/Should Be Happy It's Over Because:

This Break Up Has Made Me:

Today, I Struggle With

But I Will Conquer It Today By:

Mood:

What Do I Need Today:

How Will I Get What I Need Today:

I Use To Think

But Now I Know:

I Will Stop Wondering:

I Will Start Believing:

WHAT DO I NEED?

Date:

Today I Want God To Know:

I'm Happy/Should Be Happy It's Over Because:

This Break Up Has Made Me:

Today, I Struggle With

But I Will Conquer It Today By:

Mood:

What Do I Need Today:

How Will I Get What I Need Today:

I Use To Think

But Now I Know:

I Will Stop Wondering:

I Will Start Believing:

WHAT DO I NEED?

Date:

Mood:

Today I Want God To Know:

What Do I Need Today:

I'm Happy/Should Be Happy It's Over Because:

How Will I Get What I Need Today:

This Break Up Has Made Me:

I Use To Think

Today, I Struggle With

But Now I Know:

But I Will Conquer It Today By:

I Will Stop Wondering:

I Will Start Believing:

WHAT DO I NEED?

Date:

Today I Want God To Know:

I'm Happy/Should Be Happy It's Over Because:

This Break Up Has Made Me:

Today, I Struggle With

But I Will Conquer It Today By:

Mood:

What Do I Need Today:

How Will I Get What I Need Today:

I Use To Think

But Now I Know:

I Will Stop Wondering:

I Will Start Believing:

WHAT DO I NEED?

Date:

Mood:

Today I Want God To Know:

What Do I Need Today:

I'm Happy/Should Be Happy It's Over Because:

How Will I Get What I Need Today:

This Break Up Has Made Me:

I Use To Think

Today, I Struggle With

But Now I Know:

But I Will Conquer It Today By:

I Will Stop Wondering:

I Will Start Believing:

WHAT DO I NEED?

Date:

Today I Want God To Know:

I'm Happy/Should Be Happy It's Over Because:

This Break Up Has Made Me:

Today, I Struggle With

But I Will Conquer It Today By:

Mood:

What Do I Need Today:

How Will I Get What I Need Today:

I Use To Think

But Now I Know:

I Will Stop Wondering:

I Will Start Believing:

WHAT DO I NEED?

Date:

Today I Want God To Know:

I'm Happy/Should Be Happy It's Over Because:

This Break Up Has Made Me:

Today, I Struggle With

But I Will Conquer It Today By:

Mood:

What Do I Need Today:

How Will I Get What I Need Today:

I Use To Think

But Now I Know:

I Will Stop Wondering:

I Will Start Believing:

TODAY'S MUSIC PLAYLIST THAT MAKES ME FEEL AMAZING:

1.

2.

3.

4.

5.

6.

7.

8.

GENTLE.
I'M PUTTING MY HEART BACK IN MY HANDS AND I WILL **HANDLE** IT WITH CARE.

IN MY BECOMING,

I WILL BE FLEXIBLE AND

ALERT

BECAUSE I KNOW THAT

GOD

IS USING ME.

BECAUSE
I REFUSE TO SETTLE FOR LESS,
I WILL RECEIVE THE
BEST.

WHAT DO I NEED?

Date:

Today I Want God To Know:

I'm Happy/Should Be Happy It's Over
Because:

This Break Up Has Made Me:

Today, I Struggle With

But I Will Conquer It Today By:

Mood:

What Do I Need Today:

How Will I Get What I Need Today:

I Use To Think

But Now I Know:

I Will Stop Wondering:

I Will Start Believing:

WHAT DO I NEED?

Date:

Today I Want God To Know:

I'm Happy/Should Be Happy It's Over Because:

This Break Up Has Made Me:

Today, I Struggle With

But I Will Conquer It Today By:

Mood:

What Do I Need Today:

How Will I Get What I Need Today:

I Use To Think

But Now I Know:

I Will Stop Wondering:

I Will Start Believing:

WHAT DO I NEED?

Date:

Mood:

Today I Want God To Know:

What Do I Need Today:

I'm Happy/Should Be Happy It's Over Because:

How Will I Get What I Need Today:

This Break Up Has Made Me:

I Use To Think

Today, I Struggle With

But Now I Know:

But I Will Conquer It Today By:

I Will Stop Wondering:

I Will Start Believing:

WHAT DO I NEED?

Date:

Today I Want God To Know:

I'm Happy/Should Be Happy It's Over Because:

This Break Up Has Made Me:

Today, I Struggle With

But I Will Conquer It Today By:

Mood:

What Do I Need Today:

How Will I Get What I Need Today:

I Use To Think

But Now I Know:

I Will Stop Wondering:

I Will Start Believing:

WHAT DO I NEED?

Date:

Mood:

Today I Want God To Know:

What Do I Need Today:

I'm Happy/Should Be Happy It's Over Because:

How Will I Get What I Need Today:

This Break Up Has Made Me:

I Use To Think

Today, I Struggle With

But Now I Know:

But I Will Conquer It Today By:

I Will Stop Wondering:

I Will Start Believing:

I HAVE EVERY RIGHT TO EXPECT:

1.

2.

3.

4.

5.

LOVE.
I SPEAK IT BECAUSE I
BELIEVE IN IT.

WHAT DO I NEED?

Date:

Today I Want God To Know:

I'm Happy/Should Be Happy It's Over Because:

This Break Up Has Made Me:

Today, I Struggle With

But I Will Conquer It Today By:

Mood:

What Do I Need Today:

How Will I Get What I Need Today:

I Use To Think

But Now I Know:

I Will Stop Wondering:

I Will Start Believing:

WHAT DO I NEED?

Date:

Today I Want God To Know:

I'm Happy/Should Be Happy It's Over
Because:

This Break Up Has Made Me:

Today, I Struggle With

But I Will Conquer It Today By:

Mood:

What Do I Need Today:

How Will I Get What I Need Today:

I Use To Think

But Now I Know:

I Will Stop Wondering:

I Will Start Believing:

WHAT DO I NEED?

Date:

Today I Want God To Know:

I'm Happy/Should Be Happy It's Over Because:

This Break Up Has Made Me:

Today, I Struggle With

But I Will Conquer It Today By:

Mood:

What Do I Need Today:

How Will I Get What I Need Today:

I Use To Think

But Now I Know:

I Will Stop Wondering:

I Will Start Believing:

WHAT DO I NEED?

Date: Mood:

Today I Want God To Know: What Do I Need Today:

I'm Happy/Should Be Happy It's Over   How Will I Get What I Need Today:
Because:

This Break Up Has Made Me: I Use To Think

Today, I Struggle With   But Now I Know:

But I Will Conquer It Today By: I Will Stop Wondering:

                                              I Will Start Believing:

WHAT DO I NEED?

Date:

Mood:

Today I Want God To Know:

What Do I Need Today:

I'm Happy/Should Be Happy It's Over Because:

How Will I Get What I Need Today:

This Break Up Has Made Me:

I Use To Think

Today, I Struggle With

But Now I Know:

But I Will Conquer It Today By:

I Will Stop Wondering:

I Will Start Believing:

I'LL ALWAYS BE THE

FIRST

TO CHOOSE ME.

ALWAYS.

WHAT DO I NEED?

Date:

Today I Want God To Know:

I'm Happy/Should Be Happy It's Over Because:

This Break Up Has Made Me:

Today, I Struggle With

But I Will Conquer It Today By:

Mood:

What Do I Need Today:

How Will I Get What I Need Today:

I Use To Think

But Now I Know:

I Will Stop Wondering:

I Will Start Believing:

WHAT DO I NEED?

Date:

Today I Want God To Know:

I'm Happy/Should Be Happy It's Over Because:

This Break Up Has Made Me:

Today, I Struggle With

But I Will Conquer It Today By:

Mood:

What Do I Need Today:

How Will I Get What I Need Today:

I Use To Think

But Now I Know:

I Will Stop Wondering:

I Will Start Believing:

WHAT DO I NEED?

Date:

Today I Want God To Know:

I'm Happy/Should Be Happy It's Over
Because:

This Break Up Has Made Me:

Today, I Struggle With

But I Will Conquer It Today By:

Mood:

What Do I Need Today:

How Will I Get What I Need Today:

I Use To Think

But Now I Know:

I Will Stop Wondering:

I Will Start Believing:

WHAT DO I NEED?

Date:

Mood:

Today I Want God To Know:

What Do I Need Today:

I'm Happy/Should Be Happy It's Over
Because:

How Will I Get What I Need Today:

This Break Up Has Made Me:

I Use To Think

Today, I Struggle With

But Now I Know:

But I Will Conquer It Today By:

I Will Stop Wondering:

I Will Start Believing:

WHAT DO I NEED?

Date:

Today I Want God To Know:

I'm Happy/Should Be Happy It's Over Because:

This Break Up Has Made Me:

Today, I Struggle With

But I Will Conquer It Today By:

Mood:

What Do I Need Today:

How Will I Get What I Need Today:

I Use To Think

But Now I Know:

I Will Stop Wondering:

I Will Start Believing:

WHAT DO I NEED?

Date: Mood:

Today I Want God To Know: What Do I Need Today:

I'm Happy/Should Be Happy It's Over   How Will I Get What I Need Today:
Because:

This Break Up Has Made Me: I Use To Think

Today, I Struggle With   But Now I Know:

But I Will Conquer It Today By: I Will Stop Wondering:

                                               I Will Start Believing:

WHAT DO I NEED?

Date: Mood:

Today I Want God To Know: What Do I Need Today:

I'm Happy/Should Be Happy It's Over   How Will I Get What I Need Today:
Because:

This Break Up Has Made Me: I Use To Think

Today, I Struggle With   But Now I Know:

But I Will Conquer It Today By: I Will Stop Wondering:

                                               I Will Start Believing:

WHAT DO I NEED?

Date:

Today I Want God To Know:

I'm Happy/Should Be Happy It's Over Because:

This Break Up Has Made Me:

Today, I Struggle With

But I Will Conquer It Today By:

Mood:

What Do I Need Today:

How Will I Get What I Need Today:

I Use To Think

But Now I Know:

I Will Stop Wondering:

I Will Start Believing:

I DON'T NEED TO BE **TAMED.** I NEED TO BE **LOVED.** THAT LOVE IS COMING FROM ME.

LOVE BUILDS.
LOVE SUSTAINS.
LOVE
MULTIPLIES.

WHAT DO I NEED?

Date:

Mood:

Today I Want God To Know:

What Do I Need Today:

I'm Happy/Should Be Happy It's Over Because:

How Will I Get What I Need Today:

This Break Up Has Made Me:

I Use To Think

Today, I Struggle With

But Now I Know:

But I Will Conquer It Today By:

I Will Stop Wondering:

I Will Start Believing:

WHAT DO I NEED?

Date:

Mood:

Today I Want God To Know:

What Do I Need Today:

I'm Happy/Should Be Happy It's Over Because:

How Will I Get What I Need Today:

This Break Up Has Made Me:

I Use To Think

Today, I Struggle With

But Now I Know:

But I Will Conquer It Today By:

I Will Stop Wondering:

I Will Start Believing:

WHAT DO I NEED?

Date: Mood:

Today I Want God To Know: What Do I Need Today:

I'm Happy/Should Be Happy It's Over   How Will I Get What I Need Today:
Because:

This Break Up Has Made Me: I Use To Think

Today, I Struggle With   But Now I Know:

But I Will Conquer It Today By: I Will Stop Wondering:

                                         I Will Start Believing:

WHAT DO I NEED?

Date:	Mood:
Today I Want God To Know:	What Do I Need Today:
I'm Happy/Should Be Happy It's Over Because:	How Will I Get What I Need Today:
This Break Up Has Made Me:	I Use To Think
Today, I Struggle With	But Now I Know:
But I Will Conquer It Today By:	I Will Stop Wondering:
	I Will Start Believing:

WHAT DO I NEED?

Date: Mood:

Today I Want God To Know: What Do I Need Today:

I'm Happy/Should Be Happy It's Over   How Will I Get What I Need Today:
Because:

This Break Up Has Made Me: I Use To Think

Today, I Struggle With   But Now I Know:

But I Will Conquer It Today By: I Will Stop Wondering:

                                               I Will Start Believing:

WHAT DO I NEED?

Date: Mood:

Today I Want God To Know: What Do I Need Today:

I'm Happy/Should Be Happy It's Over   How Will I Get What I Need Today:
Because:

This Break Up Has Made Me: I Use To Think

Today, I Struggle With   But Now I Know:

But I Will Conquer It Today By: I Will Stop Wondering:

                                               I Will Start Believing:

WHAT DO I NEED?

Date: Mood:

Today I Want God To Know: What Do I Need Today:

I'm Happy/Should Be Happy It's Over   How Will I Get What I Need Today:
Because:

This Break Up Has Made Me: I Use To Think

Today, I Struggle With   But Now I Know:

But I Will Conquer It Today By: I Will Stop Wondering:

                                               I Will Start Believing:

MY THREE FAVORITE QUOTES ARE:

1.

2.

3.

I OVERCAME EVERYTHING THAT TRIED TO DESTROY ME...
I THANK GOD FOR THAT.

WHAT DO I NEED?

Date:

Mood:

Today I Want God To Know:

What Do I Need Today:

I'm Happy/Should Be Happy It's Over Because:

How Will I Get What I Need Today:

This Break Up Has Made Me:

I Use To Think

Today, I Struggle With

But Now I Know:

But I Will Conquer It Today By:

I Will Stop Wondering:

I Will Start Believing:

WHAT DO I NEED?

Date:

Today I Want God To Know:

I'm Happy/Should Be Happy It's Over Because:

This Break Up Has Made Me:

Today, I Struggle With

But I Will Conquer It Today By:

Mood:

What Do I Need Today:

How Will I Get What I Need Today:

I Use To Think

But Now I Know:

I Will Stop Wondering:

I Will Start Believing:

WHAT DO I NEED?

Date:

Today I Want God To Know:

I'm Happy/Should Be Happy It's Over Because:

This Break Up Has Made Me:

Today, I Struggle With

But I Will Conquer It Today By:

Mood:

What Do I Need Today:

How Will I Get What I Need Today:

I Use To Think

But Now I Know:

I Will Stop Wondering:

I Will Start Believing:

WHAT DO I NEED?

Date:

Today I Want God To Know:

I'm Happy/Should Be Happy It's Over Because:

This Break Up Has Made Me:

Today, I Struggle With

But I Will Conquer It Today By:

Mood:

What Do I Need Today:

How Will I Get What I Need Today:

I Use To Think

But Now I Know:

I Will Stop Wondering:

I Will Start Believing:

WHAT DO I NEED?

Date:

Mood:

Today I Want God To Know:

What Do I Need Today:

I'm Happy/Should Be Happy It's Over Because:

How Will I Get What I Need Today:

This Break Up Has Made Me:

I Use To Think

Today, I Struggle With

But Now I Know:

But I Will Conquer It Today By:

I Will Stop Wondering:

I Will Start Believing:

GROWTH
IS ONE POWERFUL
BLESSING

WHAT DO I NEED?

Date:

Mood:

Today I Want God To Know:

What Do I Need Today:

I'm Happy/Should Be Happy It's Over Because:

How Will I Get What I Need Today:

This Break Up Has Made Me:

I Use To Think

Today, I Struggle With

But Now I Know:

But I Will Conquer It Today By:

I Will Stop Wondering:

I Will Start Believing:

WHAT DO I NEED?

Date:

Today I Want God To Know:

I'm Happy/Should Be Happy It's Over Because:

This Break Up Has Made Me:

Today, I Struggle With

But I Will Conquer It Today By:

Mood:

What Do I Need Today:

How Will I Get What I Need Today:

I Use To Think

But Now I Know:

I Will Stop Wondering:

I Will Start Believing:

WHAT DO I NEED?

Date:

Today I Want God To Know:

I'm Happy/Should Be Happy It's Over Because:

This Break Up Has Made Me:

Today, I Struggle With

But I Will Conquer It Today By:

Mood:

What Do I Need Today:

How Will I Get What I Need Today:

I Use To Think

But Now I Know:

I Will Stop Wondering:

I Will Start Believing:

WHAT DO I NEED?

Date:

Today I Want God To Know:

I'm Happy/Should Be Happy It's Over Because:

This Break Up Has Made Me:

Today, I Struggle With

But I Will Conquer It Today By:

Mood:

What Do I Need Today:

How Will I Get What I Need Today:

I Use To Think

But Now I Know:

I Will Stop Wondering:

I Will Start Believing:

DO YOU HOPE TO FIND SOMEONE BETTER THAN ME? I WISH YOU WOULD SO THAT YOU WILL

LEARN

THAT PERFECTION IS A

MYTH.

MAYBE YOU'LL MISS MY JAGGED EDGES AND THE PARTS OF ME THAT FELL

SHORT OF YOUR EXPECTATIONS.

WHAT DO I NEED?

Date:

Today I Want God To Know:

I'm Happy/Should Be Happy It's Over Because:

This Break Up Has Made Me:

Today, I Struggle With

But I Will Conquer It Today By:

Mood:

What Do I Need Today:

How Will I Get What I Need Today:

I Use To Think

But Now I Know:

I Will Stop Wondering:

I Will Start Believing:

WHAT DO I NEED?

Date:

Today I Want God To Know:

I'm Happy/Should Be Happy It's Over Because:

This Break Up Has Made Me:

Today, I Struggle With

But I Will Conquer It Today By:

Mood:

What Do I Need Today:

How Will I Get What I Need Today:

I Use To Think

But Now I Know:

I Will Stop Wondering:

I Will Start Believing:

WHAT DO I NEED?

Date:

Today I Want God To Know:

I'm Happy/Should Be Happy It's Over Because:

This Break Up Has Made Me:

Today, I Struggle With

But I Will Conquer It Today By:

Mood:

What Do I Need Today:

How Will I Get What I Need Today:

I Use To Think

But Now I Know:

I Will Stop Wondering:

I Will Start Believing:

WHAT DO I NEED?

Date:

Mood:

Today I Want God To Know:

What Do I Need Today:

I'm Happy/Should Be Happy It's Over Because:

How Will I Get What I Need Today:

This Break Up Has Made Me:

I Use To Think

Today, I Struggle With

But Now I Know:

But I Will Conquer It Today By:

I Will Stop Wondering:

I Will Start Believing:

WHAT DO I NEED?

Date:

Today I Want God To Know:

I'm Happy/Should Be Happy It's Over Because:

This Break Up Has Made Me:

Today, I Struggle With

But I Will Conquer It Today By:

Mood:

What Do I Need Today:

How Will I Get What I Need Today:

I Use To Think

But Now I Know:

I Will Stop Wondering:

I Will Start Believing:

WHAT DO I NEED?

Date:

Today I Want God To Know:

I'm Happy/Should Be Happy It's Over Because:

This Break Up Has Made Me:

Today, I Struggle With

But I Will Conquer It Today By:

Mood:

What Do I Need Today:

How Will I Get What I Need Today:

I Use To Think

But Now I Know:

I Will Stop Wondering:

I Will Start Believing:

THE NEXT FEW DAYS I WILL ENJOY:

1.

2.

3.

4.

5.

MY PEACE OF MIND......
IT JUST MEANS MORE TO ME.

WHAT DO I NEED?

Date:

Mood:

Today I Want God To Know:

What Do I Need Today:

I'm Happy/Should Be Happy It's Over Because:

How Will I Get What I Need Today:

This Break Up Has Made Me:

I Use To Think

Today, I Struggle With

But Now I Know:

But I Will Conquer It Today By:

I Will Stop Wondering:

I Will Start Believing:

WHAT DO I NEED?

Date:

Today I Want God To Know:

I'm Happy/Should Be Happy It's Over Because:

This Break Up Has Made Me:

Today, I Struggle With

But I Will Conquer It Today By:

Mood:

What Do I Need Today:

How Will I Get What I Need Today:

I Use To Think

But Now I Know:

I Will Stop Wondering:

I Will Start Believing:

WHAT DO I NEED?

Date:

Today I Want God To Know:

I'm Happy/Should Be Happy It's Over Because:

This Break Up Has Made Me:

Today, I Struggle With

But I Will Conquer It Today By:

Mood:

What Do I Need Today:

How Will I Get What I Need Today:

I Use To Think

But Now I Know:

I Will Stop Wondering:

I Will Start Believing:

WHAT DO I NEED?

Date:

Today I Want God To Know:

I'm Happy/Should Be Happy It's Over Because:

This Break Up Has Made Me:

Today, I Struggle With

But I Will Conquer It Today By:

Mood:

What Do I Need Today:

How Will I Get What I Need Today:

I Use To Think

But Now I Know:

I Will Stop Wondering:

I Will Start Believing:

ACKNOWLEDGING THAT SOMETHING IS MISSING.
WORKING HARD TO RECAPTURE WHAT WAS LOST.
LETTING TIME HEAL.
RISING AFTER A HEALING.
SEEKING OUT THAT PERSON YOU WERE YESTERDAY.
BECOMING GREATER THAN YOUR FORMER SELF.
CONQUERING THE FEAR OF AN UNKNOWN FUTURE.
TAKING BOLD STEPS TOWARDS TOMORROW AND
ETERNITY.
DELIBERATELY FINDING HAPPINESS IN THE LITTLE
THINGS.
MAKING A FIST STRONG ENOUGH TO HOLD WHATEVER
HAPPINESS CAN BE GRABBED.
BLOOMING AFTER A DROUGHT.
JEALOUSLY GUARDING YOUR COLOURFUL GROWTH.
AN ADVENTURE INTO TOMORROW.
AN OPEN MIND TOWARDS THE THINGS AND PEOPLE
THAT MAY BE ENCOUNTERED ALONG THE JOURNEY.
TAKING STOCK.
CUTTING LOSSES.
MOUNTING THOSE ROCKS THAT MADE YOU STUMBLE.
PLANTING A FLAG OF VICTORY ON THESE ROCKS.
ADMITTING YOUR FAILURES.
ACKNOWLEDGING DEFEAT.
SHRUGGING OUT OF EMOTIONAL SHACKLES THAT
HELD YOU DOWN.
NOT BEING AFRAID OF A PAST THAT LEFT YOU
BLEEDING.
FACING ANCIENT DEMONS AND STRIKING THEM DOWN.
KNOWING THAT "IMPOSSIBLE" IS NOT A REAL WORD.
ACCEPTING THAT IN ORDER TO RECLAIM.

WHAT DO I NEED?

Date:

Today I Want God To Know:

I'm Happy/Should Be Happy It's Over Because:

This Break Up Has Made Me:

Today, I Struggle With

But I Will Conquer It Today By:

Mood:

What Do I Need Today:

How Will I Get What I Need Today:

I Use To Think

But Now I Know:

I Will Stop Wondering:

I Will Start Believing:

WHAT DO I NEED?

Date: Mood:

Today I Want God To Know: What Do I Need Today:

I'm Happy/Should Be Happy It's Over   How Will I Get What I Need Today:
Because:

This Break Up Has Made Me: I Use To Think

Today, I Struggle With   But Now I Know:

But I Will Conquer It Today By: I Will Stop Wondering:

                                             I Will Start Believing:

WHAT DO I NEED?

Date:

Today I Want God To Know:

I'm Happy/Should Be Happy It's Over Because:

This Break Up Has Made Me:

Today, I Struggle With

But I Will Conquer It Today By:

Mood:

What Do I Need Today:

How Will I Get What I Need Today:

I Use To Think

But Now I Know:

I Will Stop Wondering:

I Will Start Believing:

WHAT DO I NEED?

Date:

Today I Want God To Know:

I'm Happy/Should Be Happy It's Over Because:

This Break Up Has Made Me:

Today, I Struggle With

But I Will Conquer It Today By:

Mood:

What Do I Need Today:

How Will I Get What I Need Today:

I Use To Think

But Now I Know:

I Will Stop Wondering:

I Will Start Believing:

WHAT DO I NEED?

Date:

Today I Want God To Know:

I'm Happy/Should Be Happy It's Over Because:

This Break Up Has Made Me:

Today, I Struggle With

But I Will Conquer It Today By:

Mood:

What Do I Need Today:

How Will I Get What I Need Today:

I Use To Think

But Now I Know:

I Will Stop Wondering:

I Will Start Believing:

I HAVE TO RECLAIM.
TO TAKE BACK ALL THE PIECES OF

MYSELF

THAT GOT LOST WHEN I SHATTERED INTO A

MILLION SPLINTERS.

SO, I HAVE TO START AT THE BEGINNING,
AT THAT POINT WHEN YOU CAME INTO ME AND

BECAME A PART OF ME,

JUST LIKE ANOTHER LAYER OF MY SKIN.

SOMETIMES

WHEN LOVE COMES IT REALLY COMES.
BUT THIS TIME I WON'T LOSE MYSELF.
I'VE LEARNED SO MUCH THAT I KNOW THAT I WILL BE ALRIGHT.

NO RELATIONSHIP IS WASTED.

FIND THE LESSONS IN A FAILED LOVE **AND LEARN THEM THOROUGHLY.** DO NOT LET THE FEAR OF THE UNKNOWN

CAUSE

YOU TO HOLD ON TO PAIN **DISGUISED AS LOVE.**

WHAT DO I NEED?

Date:

Mood:

Today I Want God To Know:

What Do I Need Today:

I'm Happy/Should Be Happy It's Over Because:

How Will I Get What I Need Today:

This Break Up Has Made Me:

I Use To Think

Today, I Struggle With

But Now I Know:

But I Will Conquer It Today By:

I Will Stop Wondering:

I Will Start Believing:

WHAT DO I NEED?

Date:

Today I Want God To Know:

I'm Happy/Should Be Happy It's Over Because:

This Break Up Has Made Me:

Today, I Struggle With

But I Will Conquer It Today By:

Mood:

What Do I Need Today:

How Will I Get What I Need Today:

I Use To Think

But Now I Know:

I Will Stop Wondering:

I Will Start Believing:

WHAT DO I NEED?

Date:

Today I Want God To Know:

I'm Happy/Should Be Happy It's Over Because:

This Break Up Has Made Me:

Today, I Struggle With

But I Will Conquer It Today By:

Mood:

What Do I Need Today:

How Will I Get What I Need Today:

I Use To Think

But Now I Know:

I Will Stop Wondering:

I Will Start Believing:

WHAT DO I NEED?

Date:

Today I Want God To Know:

I'm Happy/Should Be Happy It's Over Because:

This Break Up Has Made Me:

Today, I Struggle With

But I Will Conquer It Today By:

Mood:

What Do I Need Today:

How Will I Get What I Need Today:

I Use To Think

But Now I Know:

I Will Stop Wondering:

I Will Start Believing:

SECTION TWO:

TIME FOR A CHANGE!

TIME FOR A CHANGE!

Date:

Today I Affirm:

Today I Realized That I Am:

Today I Will No Longer Believe:

Today I Am Choosing To Change:

Mood:

I Traded What Wasn't For Me For:

I Deserve

And I Will Get It By:

Even When I Fall, I Get Up Knowing That:

TIME FOR A CHANGE!

Date:

Today I Affirm:

Today I Realized That I Am:

Today I Will No Longer Believe:

Today I Am Choosing To Change:

Mood:

I Traded What Wasn't For Me For:

I Deserve

And I Will Get It By:

Even When I Fall, I Get Up Knowing That:

TIME FOR A CHANGE!

Date:

Today I Affirm:

Today I Realized That I Am:

Today I Will No Longer Believe:

Today I Am Choosing To Change:

Mood:

I Traded What Wasn't For Me For:

I Deserve

And I Will Get It By:

Even When I Fall, I Get Up Knowing That:

HAPPY ATTRACTS HAPPY. THAT'S WHY I CAN'T KEEP **HURT PEOPLE** WHO WILL HURT ME **AROUND.**

TIME FOR A CHANGE!

Date:

Today I Affirm:

Today I Realized That I Am:

Today I Will No Longer Believe:

Today I Am Choosing To Change:

Mood:

I Traded What Wasn't For Me For:

I Deserve

And I Will Get It By:

Even When I Fall, I Get Up Knowing That:

TIME FOR A CHANGE!

Date:

Today I Affirm:

Today I Realized That I Am:

Today I Will No Longer Believe:

Today I Am Choosing To Change:

Mood:

I Traded What Wasn't For Me For:

I Deserve

And I Will Get It By:

Even When I Fall, I Get Up Knowing That:

TIME FOR A CHANGE!

Date: Mood:

Today I Affirm: I Traded What Wasn't For Me For:

Today I Realized That I Am: I Deserve

Today I Will No Longer Believe: And I Will Get It By:

Today I Am Choosing To Change: Even When I Fall, I Get Up Knowing That:

TIME FOR A CHANGE!

Date:

Today I Affirm:

Today I Realized That I Am:

Today I Will No Longer Believe:

Today I Am Choosing To Change:

Mood:

I Traded What Wasn't For Me For:

I Deserve

And I Will Get It By:

Even When I Fall, I Get Up Knowing That:

TIME FOR A CHANGE!

Date:

Today I Affirm:

Today I Realized That I Am:

Today I Will No Longer Believe:

Today I Am Choosing To Change:

Mood:

I Traded What Wasn't For Me For:

I Deserve

And I Will Get It By:

Even When I Fall, I Get Up Knowing That:

TIME FOR A CHANGE!

Date:

Today I Affirm:

Today I Realized That I Am:

Today I Will No Longer Believe:

Today I Am Choosing To Change:

Mood:

I Traded What Wasn't For Me For:

I Deserve

And I Will Get It By:

Even When I Fall, I Get Up Knowing That:

TIME FOR A CHANGE!

Date:

Today I Affirm:

Today I Realized That I Am:

Today I Will No Longer Believe:

Today I Am Choosing To Change:

Mood:

I Traded What Wasn't For Me For:

I Deserve

And I Will Get It By:

Even When I Fall, I Get Up Knowing That:

YOU WILL FIND ANOTHER

LOVE.

YOU NEED TO LET GO OF THE PAIN
AND TRUST THAT GOD HAS GOT YOU,
AND THAT HIS PLANS FOR YOU ARE

PERFECT.

OPEN UP YOUR HANDS AND LET GO OF THE PAIN
AND THE TEARS, ONLY THEN WILL GOD TAKE YOUR

EMPTY HAND IN HIS

AND LEAD YOU TO THE ONE HE HAS

PREPARED FOR YOU.

LETTING GO SHOWS THAT YOU HAVE FAITH IN

GOD.

FAITH MOVES GOD.

HOW WILL THE RIGHT LOVE FIND YOU AND TAKE YOUR HAND IF YOU ARE

TIGHTLY HOLDING

ON TO SOMETHING ELSE?

TIME FOR A CHANGE!

Date:

Today I Affirm:

Today I Realized That I Am:

Today I Will No Longer Believe:

Today I Am Choosing To Change:

Mood:

I Traded What Wasn't For Me For:

I Deserve

And I Will Get It By:

Even When I Fall, I Get Up Knowing That:

TIME FOR A CHANGE!

Date:

Today I Affirm:

Today I Realized That I Am:

Today I Will No Longer Believe:

Today I Am Choosing To Change:

Mood:

I Traded What Wasn't For Me For:

I Deserve

And I Will Get It By:

Even When I Fall, I Get Up Knowing That:

TIME FOR A CHANGE!

Date:

Today I Affirm:

Today I Realized That I Am:

Today I Will No Longer Believe:

Today I Am Choosing To Change:

Mood:

I Traded What Wasn't For Me For:

I Deserve

And I Will Get It By:

Even When I Fall, I Get Up Knowing That:

TIME FOR A CHANGE!

Date:

Today I Affirm:

Today I Realized That I Am:

Today I Will No Longer Believe:

Today I Am Choosing To Change:

Mood:

I Traded What Wasn't For Me For:

I Deserve

And I Will Get It By:

Even When I Fall, I Get Up Knowing That:

TIME FOR A CHANGE!

Date:

Today I Affirm:

Today I Realized That I Am:

Today I Will No Longer Believe:

Today I Am Choosing To Change:

Mood:

I Traded What Wasn't For Me For:

I Deserve

And I Will Get It By:

Even When I Fall, I Get Up Knowing That:

THE NEXT FEW DAYS I WILL ENJOY:

1.

2.

3.

4.

5.

TELL THE TRUTH TO YOURSELF.
NOW MOVE FORWARD

TIME FOR A CHANGE!

Date:

Today I Affirm:

Today I Realized That I Am:

Today I Will No Longer Believe:

Today I Am Choosing To Change:

Mood:

I Traded What Wasn't For Me For:

I Deserve

And I Will Get It By:

Even When I Fall, I Get Up Knowing That:

TIME FOR A CHANGE!

Date:

Today I Affirm:

Today I Realized That I Am:

Today I Will No Longer Believe:

Today I Am Choosing To Change:

Mood:

I Traded What Wasn't For Me For:

I Deserve

And I Will Get It By:

Even When I Fall, I Get Up Knowing That:

TIME FOR A CHANGE!

Date:

Today I Affirm:

Today I Realized That I Am:

Today I Will No Longer Believe:

Today I Am Choosing To Change:

Mood:

I Traded What Wasn't For Me For:

I Deserve

And I Will Get It By:

Even When I Fall, I Get Up Knowing That:

TIME FOR A CHANGE!

Date: | Mood:

Today I Affirm: | I Traded What Wasn't For Me For:

Today I Realized That I Am: | I Deserve

Today I Will No Longer Believe: | And I Will Get It By:

Today I Am Choosing To Change: | Even When I Fall, I Get Up Knowing That:

THAT RELATIONSHIP WAS NOT **WASTED.** YOU NEEDED THAT FAILED LOVE TO LEARN WHAT REAL **LOVE** MEANS SO THAT WHEN THE RIGHT ONE COMES, YOU WILL APPRECIATE THE **REAL LOVE** FOR WHAT IT IS. LOVE SHOULD NOT MAKE YOU CRY AND BLEED.

WALK AWAY
FROM PAIN DISGUISED AS LOVE.
TAKE A DEEP BREATH
AND SET THE PAST FREE.
YOUR REAL LOVE IS ALREADY
ON THE WAY.

TIME FOR A CHANGE!

Date:

Today I Affirm:

Today I Realized That I Am:

Today I Will No Longer Believe:

Today I Am Choosing To Change:

Mood:

I Traded What Wasn't For Me For:

I Deserve

And I Will Get It By:

Even When I Fall, I Get Up Knowing That:

TIME FOR A CHANGE!

Date:

Today I Affirm:

Today I Realized That I Am:

Today I Will No Longer Believe:

Today I Am Choosing To Change:

Mood:

I Traded What Wasn't For Me For:

I Deserve

And I Will Get It By:

Even When I Fall, I Get Up Knowing That:

TIME FOR A CHANGE!

Date:

Today I Affirm:

Today I Realized That I Am:

Today I Will No Longer Believe:

Today I Am Choosing To Change:

Mood:

I Traded What Wasn't For Me For:

I Deserve

And I Will Get It By:

Even When I Fall, I Get Up Knowing That:

I AM DIFFERENT BECAUSE:

YOU ARE NEVER "TOO MUCH" OF ANYTHING FOR THE RIGHT PERSON.

TIME FOR A CHANGE!

Date: Mood:

Today I Affirm: I Traded What Wasn't For Me For:

Today I Realized That I Am: I Deserve

Today I Will No Longer Believe: And I Will Get It By:

Today I Am Choosing To Change: Even When I Fall, I Get Up Knowing That:

TIME FOR A CHANGE!

Date:

Today I Affirm:

Today I Realized That I Am:

Today I Will No Longer Believe:

Today I Am Choosing To Change:

Mood:

I Traded What Wasn't For Me For:

I Deserve

And I Will Get It By:

Even When I Fall, I Get Up Knowing That:

TIME FOR A CHANGE!

Date:

Mood:

Today I Affirm:

I Traded What Wasn't For Me For:

Today I Realized That I Am:

I Deserve

Today I Will No Longer Believe:

And I Will Get It By:

Today I Am Choosing To Change:

Even When I Fall, I Get Up Knowing That:

TIME FOR A CHANGE!

Date:

Today I Affirm:

Mood:

I Traded What Wasn't For Me For:

Today I Realized That I Am:

I Deserve

Today I Will No Longer Believe:

And I Will Get It By:

Today I Am Choosing To Change:

Even When I Fall, I Get Up Knowing That:

TIME FOR A CHANGE!

Date: Mood:

Today I Affirm: I Traded What Wasn't For Me For:

Today I Realized That I Am: I Deserve

Today I Will No Longer Believe: And I Will Get It By:

Today I Am Choosing To Change: Even When I Fall, I Get Up Knowing That:

TIME FOR A CHANGE!

Date:

Today I Affirm:

Today I Realized That I Am:

Today I Will No Longer Believe:

Today I Am Choosing To Change:

Mood:

I Traded What Wasn't For Me For:

I Deserve

And I Will Get It By:

Even When I Fall, I Get Up Knowing That:

TIME FOR A CHANGE!

Date:

Today I Affirm:

Today I Realized That I Am:

Today I Will No Longer Believe:

Today I Am Choosing To Change:

Mood:

I Traded What Wasn't For Me For:

I Deserve

And I Will Get It By:

Even When I Fall, I Get Up Knowing That:

TIME FOR A CHANGE!

Date: | Mood:

Today I Affirm: | I Traded What Wasn't For Me For:

Today I Realized That I Am: | I Deserve

Today I Will No Longer Believe: | And I Will Get It By:

Today I Am Choosing To Change: | Even When I Fall, I Get Up Knowing That:

TIME FOR A CHANGE!

Date: Mood:

Today I Affirm: I Traded What Wasn't For Me For:

Today I Realized That I Am: I Deserve

Today I Will No Longer Believe: And I Will Get It By:

Today I Am Choosing To Change: Even When I Fall, I Get Up Knowing That:

TIME FOR A CHANGE!

Date: Mood:

Today I Affirm: I Traded What Wasn't For Me For:

Today I Realized That I Am: I Deserve

Today I Will No Longer Believe: And I Will Get It By:

Today I Am Choosing To Change: Even When I Fall, I Get Up Knowing That:

IT MAY LOOK LIKE YOU HAVE FAILED AT

LOVE,

BUT YOU ARE DEFINITELY NOT A FAILURE.
YOUR OLD LOVE IS GONE AND YOUR HEART IS BROKEN,
BUT IT IS NOT A MISTAKE.
GOD, IN HIS INFINITE MERCIES,
HAS BETTER PLANS FOR YOU,
AND THIS PLAN INCLUDES THE PERFECT LOVE FOR YOU,
THE ONE WHO WILL MAKE YOU WONDER WHY YOU HAD
EVEN BOTHERED WITH ANY OTHER PERSON IN THE PAST,
WHO WILL SHOW YOU THE ALL-ENCOMPASSING POWER OF

LOVE.

TIME FOR A CHANGE!

Date:

Today I Affirm:

Today I Realized That I Am:

Today I Will No Longer Believe:

Today I Am Choosing To Change:

Mood:

I Traded What Wasn't For Me For:

I Deserve

And I Will Get It By:

Even When I Fall, I Get Up Knowing That:

TIME FOR A CHANGE!

Date:

Today I Affirm:

Today I Realized That I Am:

Today I Will No Longer Believe:

Today I Am Choosing To Change:

Mood:

I Traded What Wasn't For Me For:

I Deserve

And I Will Get It By:

Even When I Fall, I Get Up Knowing That:

TIME FOR A CHANGE!

Date:

Today I Affirm:

Today I Realized That I Am:

Today I Will No Longer Believe:

Today I Am Choosing To Change:

Mood:

I Traded What Wasn't For Me For:

I Deserve

And I Will Get It By:

Even When I Fall, I Get Up Knowing That:

TIME FOR A CHANGE!

Date:

Today I Affirm:

Today I Realized That I Am:

Today I Will No Longer Believe:

Today I Am Choosing To Change:

Mood:

I Traded What Wasn't For Me For:

I Deserve

And I Will Get It By:

Even When I Fall, I Get Up Knowing That:

TIME FOR A CHANGE!

Date:

Today I Affirm:

Today I Realized That I Am:

Today I Will No Longer Believe:

Today I Am Choosing To Change:

Mood:

I Traded What Wasn't For Me For:

I Deserve

And I Will Get It By:

Even When I Fall, I Get Up Knowing That:

TIME FOR A CHANGE!

Date:

Today I Affirm:

Today I Realized That I Am:

Today I Will No Longer Believe:

Today I Am Choosing To Change:

Mood:

I Traded What Wasn't For Me For:

I Deserve

And I Will Get It By:

Even When I Fall, I Get Up Knowing That:

TIME FOR A CHANGE!

Date:

Today I Affirm:

Today I Realized That I Am:

Today I Will No Longer Believe:

Today I Am Choosing To Change:

Mood:

I Traded What Wasn't For Me For:

I Deserve

And I Will Get It By:

Even When I Fall, I Get Up Knowing That:

TIME FOR A CHANGE!

Date:

Today I Affirm:

Today I Realized That I Am:

Today I Will No Longer Believe:

Today I Am Choosing To Change:

Mood:

I Traded What Wasn't For Me For:

I Deserve

And I Will Get It By:

Even When I Fall, I Get Up Knowing That:

TIME FOR A CHANGE!

Date:

Mood:

Today I Affirm:

I Traded What Wasn't For Me For:

Today I Realized That I Am:

I Deserve

Today I Will No Longer Believe:

And I Will Get It By:

Today I Am Choosing To Change:

Even When I Fall, I Get Up Knowing That:

YOU HAVE NOT LOST.
YOU ARE ONLY GETTING A
FRESH START.
BEGIN WITH FAITH AND HOPE.

TIME FOR A CHANGE!

Date:

Today I Affirm:

Today I Realized That I Am:

Today I Will No Longer Believe:

Today I Am Choosing To Change:

Mood:

I Traded What Wasn't For Me For:

I Deserve

And I Will Get It By:

Even When I Fall, I Get Up Knowing That:

TIME FOR A CHANGE!

Date:

Today I Affirm:

Today I Realized That I Am:

Today I Will No Longer Believe:

Today I Am Choosing To Change:

Mood:

I Traded What Wasn't For Me For:

I Deserve

And I Will Get It By:

Even When I Fall, I Get Up Knowing That:

TIME FOR A CHANGE!

Date: Mood:

Today I Affirm: I Traded What Wasn't For Me For:

Today I Realized That I Am: I Deserve

Today I Will No Longer Believe: And I Will Get It By:

Today I Am Choosing To Change: Even When I Fall, I Get Up Knowing That:

TIME FOR A CHANGE!

Date:

Today I Affirm:

Today I Realized That I Am:

Today I Will No Longer Believe:

Today I Am Choosing To Change:

Mood:

I Traded What Wasn't For Me For:

I Deserve

And I Will Get It By:

Even When I Fall, I Get Up Knowing That:

TIME FOR A CHANGE!

Date:

Today I Affirm:

Today I Realized That I Am:

Today I Will No Longer Believe:

Today I Am Choosing To Change:

Mood:

I Traded What Wasn't For Me For:

I Deserve

And I Will Get It By:

Even When I Fall, I Get Up Knowing That:

TIME FOR A CHANGE!

Date:

Today I Affirm:

Today I Realized That I Am:

Today I Will No Longer Believe:

Today I Am Choosing To Change:

Mood:

I Traded What Wasn't For Me For:

I Deserve

And I Will Get It By:

Even When I Fall, I Get Up Knowing That:

TIME FOR A CHANGE!

Date:

Today I Affirm:

Today I Realized That I Am:

Today I Will No Longer Believe:

Today I Am Choosing To Change:

Mood:

I Traded What Wasn't For Me For:

I Deserve

And I Will Get It By:

Even When I Fall, I Get Up Knowing That:

TIME FOR A CHANGE!

Date:

Mood:

Today I Affirm:

I Traded What Wasn't For Me For:

Today I Realized That I Am:

I Deserve

Today I Will No Longer Believe:

And I Will Get It By:

Today I Am Choosing To Change:

Even When I Fall, I Get Up Knowing That:

TIME FOR A CHANGE!

Date:

Today I Affirm:

Today I Realized That I Am:

Today I Will No Longer Believe:

Today I Am Choosing To Change:

Mood:

I Traded What Wasn't For Me For:

I Deserve

And I Will Get It By:

Even When I Fall, I Get Up Knowing That:

TIME FOR A CHANGE!

Date:

Today I Affirm:

Today I Realized That I Am:

Today I Will No Longer Believe:

Today I Am Choosing To Change:

Mood:

I Traded What Wasn't For Me For:

I Deserve

And I Will Get It By:

Even When I Fall, I Get Up Knowing That:

THIS IS A TIME OF
RENEWAL

I CANNOT BE WITH 'THE ONE' THAT WAS CREATED JUST FOR ME
IF MY MIND IS NOT RECONDITIONED TO SUIT THIS

COMING GREAT LOVE.

I AM BEING BROKEN DOWN SO THAT I WILL BE MADE

PERFECT.

THIS PAIN IS THE FIRE OF REFINEMENT
THAT GOLD HAS TO PASS THROUGH.
WHEN THE ONE GOD HAS DESTINED FOR ME COMES,
THAT PERSON WILL FIND ME PERFECT FOR THEM.

THIS TIME,

I WILL NOT FEEL LIKE I ARE

STANDING ON SHAKY GROUND.

I WILL LEARN THAT REAL LOVE IS STRONG AND UNSHAKEABLE
AND THAT IT WILL NOT LEAVE ME SWAYING IN THE WIND.

I AM VALUABLE AND WORTHY.
I AM BEAUTIFUL AND UNIQUE.
I AM LOVABLE AND GREAT.

TIME FOR A CHANGE!

Date:

Today I Affirm:

Today I Realized That I Am:

Today I Will No Longer Believe:

Today I Am Choosing To Change:

Mood:

I Traded What Wasn't For Me For:

I Deserve

And I Will Get It By:

Even When I Fall, I Get Up Knowing That:

TIME FOR A CHANGE!

Date:

Today I Affirm:

Today I Realized That I Am:

Today I Will No Longer Believe:

Today I Am Choosing To Change:

Mood:

I Traded What Wasn't For Me For:

I Deserve

And I Will Get It By:

Even When I Fall, I Get Up Knowing That:

TIME FOR A CHANGE!

Date:

Today I Affirm:

Today I Realized That I Am:

Today I Will No Longer Believe:

Today I Am Choosing To Change:

Mood:

I Traded What Wasn't For Me For:

I Deserve

And I Will Get It By:

Even When I Fall, I Get Up Knowing That:

TIME FOR A CHANGE!

Date:

Today I Affirm:

Today I Realized That I Am:

Today I Will No Longer Believe:

Today I Am Choosing To Change:

Mood:

I Traded What Wasn't For Me For:

I Deserve

And I Will Get It By:

Even When I Fall, I Get Up Knowing That:

TIME FOR A CHANGE!

Date:

Today I Affirm:

Today I Realized That I Am:

Today I Will No Longer Believe:

Today I Am Choosing To Change:

Mood:

I Traded What Wasn't For Me For:

I Deserve

And I Will Get It By:

Even When I Fall, I Get Up Knowing That:

TIME FOR A CHANGE!

Date: Mood:

Today I Affirm: I Traded What Wasn't For Me For:

Today I Realized That I Am: I Deserve

Today I Will No Longer Believe: And I Will Get It By:

Today I Am Choosing To Change: Even When I Fall, I Get Up Knowing That:

TIME FOR A CHANGE!

Date: Mood:

Today I Affirm: I Traded What Wasn't For Me For:

Today I Realized That I Am: I Deserve

Today I Will No Longer Believe: And I Will Get It By:

Today I Am Choosing To Change: Even When I Fall, I Get Up Knowing That:

VALUABLE ADVICE MY MOM USE TO SAY:

I WILL REMEMBER THE PROMISES I MADE TO

MYSELF

TIME FOR A CHANGE!

Date:

Today I Affirm:

Today I Realized That I Am:

Today I Will No Longer Believe:

Today I Am Choosing To Change:

Mood:

I Traded What Wasn't For Me For:

I Deserve

And I Will Get It By:

Even When I Fall, I Get Up Knowing That:

TIME FOR A CHANGE!

Date:

Today I Affirm:

Today I Realized That I Am:

Today I Will No Longer Believe:

Today I Am Choosing To Change:

Mood:

I Traded What Wasn't For Me For:

I Deserve

And I Will Get It By:

Even When I Fall, I Get Up Knowing That:

SECTION THREE:

WHAT I WILL RECEIVE

WHAT I WILL RECEIVE

Date:

What I Want God To Know:

What Makes Me So Special:

I Am Grateful For:

I Know I Will Receive:

Mood:

Today I Am Free And Open To Accept:

I Am Worthy Of:

Today I Made Room To Receive Love By:

Today I Am At A Place Where I:

Today's Blessing Came In The Form Of:

WHAT I WILL RECEIVE

Date: Mood:

What I Want God To Know: Today I Am Free And Open To Accept:

What Makes Me So Special: I Am Worthy Of:

I Am Grateful For: Today I Made Room To Receive Love By:

I Know I Will Receive: Today I Am At A Place Where I:

                                               Today's Blessing Came In The Form Of:

WHAT I WILL RECEIVE

Date:

What I Want God To Know:

What Makes Me So Special:

I Am Grateful For:

I Know I Will Receive:

Mood:

Today I Am Free And Open To Accept:

I Am Worthy Of:

Today I Made Room To Receive Love By:

Today I Am At A Place Where I:

Today's Blessing Came In The Form Of:

WHAT I WILL RECEIVE

Date:

What I Want God To Know:

What Makes Me So Special:

I Am Grateful For:

I Know I Will Receive:

Mood:

Today I Am Free And Open To Accept:

I Am Worthy Of:

Today I Made Room To Receive Love By:

Today I Am At A Place Where I:

Today's Blessing Came In The Form Of:

WHAT I WILL RECEIVE

Date:

What I Want God To Know:

What Makes Me So Special:

I Am Grateful For:

I Know I Will Receive:

Mood:

Today I Am Free And Open To Accept:

I Am Worthy Of:

Today I Made Room To Receive Love By:

Today I Am At A Place Where I:

Today's Blessing Came In The Form Of:

BEFORE YOU ENTER IN IT,

MAKE SURE YOU ARE COMING INTO IT WITH

LOVE.

– MY RELATIONSHIP WITH ME

WHAT I WILL RECEIVE

Date:

What I Want God To Know:

What Makes Me So Special:

I Am Grateful For:

I Know I Will Receive:

Mood:

Today I Am Free And Open To Accept:

I Am Worthy Of:

Today I Made Room To Receive Love By:

Today I Am At A Place Where I:

Today's Blessing Came In The Form Of:

WHAT I WILL RECEIVE

Date:

What I Want God To Know:

What Makes Me So Special:

I Am Grateful For:

I Know I Will Receive:

Mood:

Today I Am Free And Open To Accept:

I Am Worthy Of:

Today I Made Room To Receive Love By:

Today I Am At A Place Where I:

Today's Blessing Came In The Form Of:

WHAT I WILL RECEIVE

Date:

What I Want God To Know:

What Makes Me So Special:

I Am Grateful For:

I Know I Will Receive:

Mood:

Today I Am Free And Open To Accept:

I Am Worthy Of:

Today I Made Room To Receive Love By:

Today I Am At A Place Where I:

Today's Blessing Came In The Form Of:

WHAT I WILL RECEIVE

Date:

What I Want God To Know:

What Makes Me So Special:

I Am Grateful For:

I Know I Will Receive:

Mood:

Today I Am Free And Open To Accept:

I Am Worthy Of:

Today I Made Room To Receive Love By:

Today I Am At A Place Where I:

Today's Blessing Came In The Form Of:

WHAT I WILL RECEIVE

Date:

What I Want God To Know:

What Makes Me So Special:

I Am Grateful For:

I Know I Will Receive:

Mood:

Today I Am Free And Open To Accept:

I Am Worthy Of:

Today I Made Room To Receive Love By:

Today I Am At A Place Where I:

Today's Blessing Came In The Form Of:

MY FIVE FAVORITE SCENTS THAT MAKE ME FEEL GOOD ARE:

1.

2.

3.

4.

5.

A SHIFT IS HAPPENING IN MY
FAVOR.

WHAT I WILL RECEIVE

Date:

What I Want God To Know:

What Makes Me So Special:

I Am Grateful For:

I Know I Will Receive:

Mood:

Today I Am Free And Open To Accept:

I Am Worthy Of:

Today I Made Room To Receive Love By:

Today I Am At A Place Where I:

Today's Blessing Came In The Form Of:

WHAT I WILL RECEIVE

Date:

What I Want God To Know:

What Makes Me So Special:

I Am Grateful For:

I Know I Will Receive:

Mood:

Today I Am Free And Open To Accept:

I Am Worthy Of:

Today I Made Room To Receive Love By:

Today I Am At A Place Where I:

Today's Blessing Came In The Form Of:

WHAT I WILL RECEIVE

Date:

What I Want God To Know:

What Makes Me So Special:

I Am Grateful For:

I Know I Will Receive:

Mood:

Today I Am Free And Open To Accept:

I Am Worthy Of:

Today I Made Room To Receive Love By:

Today I Am At A Place Where I:

Today's Blessing Came In The Form Of:

WHAT I WILL RECEIVE

Date:

What I Want God To Know:

What Makes Me So Special:

I Am Grateful For:

I Know I Will Receive:

Mood:

Today I Am Free And Open To Accept:

I Am Worthy Of:

Today I Made Room To Receive Love By:

Today I Am At A Place Where I:

Today's Blessing Came In The Form Of:

WHAT I WILL RECEIVE

Date:

What I Want God To Know:

What Makes Me So Special:

I Am Grateful For:

I Know I Will Receive:

Mood:

Today I Am Free And Open To Accept:

I Am Worthy Of:

Today I Made Room To Receive Love By:

Today I Am At A Place Where I:

Today's Blessing Came In The Form Of:

WHAT I WILL RECEIVE

Date:

What I Want God To Know:

What Makes Me So Special:

I Am Grateful For:

I Know I Will Receive:

Mood:

Today I Am Free And Open To Accept:

I Am Worthy Of:

Today I Made Room To Receive Love By:

Today I Am At A Place Where I:

Today's Blessing Came In The Form Of:

177

WHEN THE RIGHT PERSON COMES, THEY WILL FIND YOU PERFECT,

UNIQUE AND LOVELY.

THEY WILL LOVE YOU WITH PASSION.

THEY WILL MAKE YOU FEEL ALL THE GREAT THINGS THAT YOU ARE.

YOU WILL NEVER WONDER AGAIN IF YOU ARE

BEAUTIFUL ENOUGH,
GOOD ENOUGH,
OR WORTHY OF LOVE.

THE LOVE OF YOUR LIFE WILL MAKE YOUR FACE SHINE.

IT WILL MAKE YOUR SMILE PERMANENT
IT WILL MAKE YOU GLOW.

YOUR BEST COMEBACK IS A

SMILE

WITH A PRAYER

WHAT I WILL RECEIVE

Date: Mood:

What I Want God To Know: Today I Am Free And Open To Accept:

What Makes Me So Special: I Am Worthy Of:

I Am Grateful For: Today I Made Room To Receive Love By:

I Know I Will Receive: Today I Am At A Place Where I:

                                         Today's Blessing Came In The Form Of:

WHAT I WILL RECEIVE

Date: Mood:

What I Want God To Know: Today I Am Free And Open To Accept:

What Makes Me So Special: I Am Worthy Of:

I Am Grateful For: Today I Made Room To Receive Love By:

I Know I Will Receive: Today I Am At A Place Where I:

                                             Today's Blessing Came In The Form Of:

WHAT I WILL RECEIVE

Date:

What I Want God To Know:

What Makes Me So Special:

I Am Grateful For:

I Know I Will Receive:

Mood:

Today I Am Free And Open To Accept:

I Am Worthy Of:

Today I Made Room To Receive Love By:

Today I Am At A Place Where I:

Today's Blessing Came In The Form Of:

LOVE IS GRATITUDE.
GRATITUDE IS A CHARACTERISTIC OF LOVE.

WHAT I WILL RECEIVE

Date:

What I Want God To Know:

What Makes Me So Special:

I Am Grateful For:

I Know I Will Receive:

Mood:

Today I Am Free And Open To Accept:

I Am Worthy Of:

Today I Made Room To Receive Love By:

Today I Am At A Place Where I:

Today's Blessing Came In The Form Of:

WHAT I WILL RECEIVE

Date:

What I Want God To Know:

What Makes Me So Special:

I Am Grateful For:

I Know I Will Receive:

Mood:

Today I Am Free And Open To Accept:

I Am Worthy Of:

Today I Made Room To Receive Love By:

Today I Am At A Place Where I:

Today's Blessing Came In The Form Of:

WHAT I WILL RECEIVE

Date:

What I Want God To Know:

What Makes Me So Special:

I Am Grateful For:

I Know I Will Receive:

Mood:

Today I Am Free And Open To Accept:

I Am Worthy Of:

Today I Made Room To Receive Love By:

Today I Am At A Place Where I:

Today's Blessing Came In The Form Of:

WHAT I WILL RECEIVE

Date:

What I Want God To Know:

What Makes Me So Special:

I Am Grateful For:

I Know I Will Receive:

Mood:

Today I Am Free And Open To Accept:

I Am Worthy Of:

Today I Made Room To Receive Love By:

Today I Am At A Place Where I:

Today's Blessing Came In The Form Of:

WHAT I WILL RECEIVE

Date:

What I Want God To Know:

What Makes Me So Special:

I Am Grateful For:

I Know I Will Receive:

Mood:

Today I Am Free And Open To Accept:

I Am Worthy Of:

Today I Made Room To Receive Love By:

Today I Am At A Place Where I:

Today's Blessing Came In The Form Of:

WHAT I WILL RECEIVE

Date:

What I Want God To Know:

What Makes Me So Special:

I Am Grateful For:

I Know I Will Receive:

Mood:

Today I Am Free And Open To Accept:

I Am Worthy Of:

Today I Made Room To Receive Love By:

Today I Am At A Place Where I:

Today's Blessing Came In The Form Of:

WHAT I WILL RECEIVE

Date:

What I Want God To Know:

What Makes Me So Special:

I Am Grateful For:

I Know I Will Receive:

Mood:

Today I Am Free And Open To Accept:

I Am Worthy Of:

Today I Made Room To Receive Love By:

Today I Am At A Place Where I:

Today's Blessing Came In The Form Of:

JUST BECAUSE THEY DIDN'T KNOW WHAT TO DO WITH MY

LOVE,

DOESN'T MEAN I HAVE STOPPED LOVING.

MY FOCUS IS JUST
REDIRECTED.

WHAT I WILL RECEIVE

Date:

What I Want God To Know:

What Makes Me So Special:

I Am Grateful For:

I Know I Will Receive:

Mood:

Today I Am Free And Open To Accept:

I Am Worthy Of:

Today I Made Room To Receive Love By:

Today I Am At A Place Where I:

Today's Blessing Came In The Form Of:

WHAT I WILL RECEIVE

Date:

What I Want God To Know:

What Makes Me So Special:

I Am Grateful For:

I Know I Will Receive:

Mood:

Today I Am Free And Open To Accept:

I Am Worthy Of:

Today I Made Room To Receive Love By:

Today I Am At A Place Where I:

Today's Blessing Came In The Form Of:

WHAT I WILL RECEIVE

Date: Mood:

What I Want God To Know: Today I Am Free And Open To Accept:

What Makes Me So Special: I Am Worthy Of:

I Am Grateful For: Today I Made Room To Receive Love By:

I Know I Will Receive: Today I Am At A Place Where I:

                                               Today's Blessing Came In The Form Of:

WHAT I WILL RECEIVE

Date: Mood:

What I Want God To Know: Today I Am Free And Open To Accept:

What Makes Me So Special: I Am Worthy Of:

I Am Grateful For: Today I Made Room To Receive Love By:

I Know I Will Receive: Today I Am At A Place Where I:

                                           Today's Blessing Came In The Form Of:

WHAT I WILL RECEIVE

Date:

What I Want God To Know:

What Makes Me So Special:

I Am Grateful For:

I Know I Will Receive:

Mood:

Today I Am Free And Open To Accept:

I Am Worthy Of:

Today I Made Room To Receive Love By:

Today I Am At A Place Where I:

Today's Blessing Came In The Form Of:

WHAT I WILL RECEIVE

Date:

What I Want God To Know:

What Makes Me So Special:

I Am Grateful For:

I Know I Will Receive:

Mood:

Today I Am Free And Open To Accept:

I Am Worthy Of:

Today I Made Room To Receive Love By:

Today I Am At A Place Where I:

Today's Blessing Came In The Form Of:

WHAT I WILL RECEIVE

Date: Mood:

What I Want God To Know: Today I Am Free And Open To Accept:

What Makes Me So Special: I Am Worthy Of:

I Am Grateful For: Today I Made Room To Receive Love By:

I Know I Will Receive: Today I Am At A Place Where I:

                                               Today's Blessing Came In The Form Of:

WHAT I WILL RECEIVE

Date:

What I Want God To Know:

What Makes Me So Special:

I Am Grateful For:

I Know I Will Receive:

Mood:

Today I Am Free And Open To Accept:

I Am Worthy Of:

Today I Made Room To Receive Love By:

Today I Am At A Place Where I:

Today's Blessing Came In The Form Of:

WHAT I WILL RECEIVE

Date:

What I Want God To Know:

What Makes Me So Special:

I Am Grateful For:

I Know I Will Receive:

Mood:

Today I Am Free And Open To Accept:

I Am Worthy Of:

Today I Made Room To Receive Love By:

Today I Am At A Place Where I:

Today's Blessing Came In The Form Of:

WHAT I WILL RECEIVE

Date:

What I Want God To Know:

What Makes Me So Special:

I Am Grateful For:

I Know I Will Receive:

Mood:

Today I Am Free And Open To Accept:

I Am Worthy Of:

Today I Made Room To Receive Love By:

Today I Am At A Place Where I:

Today's Blessing Came In The Form Of:

GO OUT AND GET WHAT YOU

WANT

SOME PEOPLE ENTER YOUR LIFE TO **MOTIVATE YOU.** THEY WERE NOT MEANT TO BE **AROUND FOREVER.**

WHAT I WILL RECEIVE

Date:

What I Want God To Know:

What Makes Me So Special:

I Am Grateful For:

I Know I Will Receive:

Mood:

Today I Am Free And Open To Accept:

I Am Worthy Of:

Today I Made Room To Receive Love By:

Today I Am At A Place Where I:

Today's Blessing Came In The Form Of:

WHAT I WILL RECEIVE

Date:

What I Want God To Know:

What Makes Me So Special:

I Am Grateful For:

I Know I Will Receive:

Mood:

Today I Am Free And Open To Accept:

I Am Worthy Of:

Today I Made Room To Receive Love By:

Today I Am At A Place Where I:

Today's Blessing Came In The Form Of:

WHAT I WILL RECEIVE

Date:

What I Want God To Know:

What Makes Me So Special:

I Am Grateful For:

I Know I Will Receive:

Mood:

Today I Am Free And Open To Accept:

I Am Worthy Of:

Today I Made Room To Receive Love By:

Today I Am At A Place Where I:

Today's Blessing Came In The Form Of:

WHAT I WILL RECEIVE

Date:

What I Want God To Know:

What Makes Me So Special:

I Am Grateful For:

I Know I Will Receive:

Mood:

Today I Am Free And Open To Accept:

I Am Worthy Of:

Today I Made Room To Receive Love By:

Today I Am At A Place Where I:

Today's Blessing Came In The Form Of:

WHAT I WILL RECEIVE

Date: Mood:

What I Want God To Know: Today I Am Free And Open To Accept:

What Makes Me So Special: I Am Worthy Of:

I Am Grateful For: Today I Made Room To Receive Love By:

I Know I Will Receive: Today I Am At A Place Where I:

                                         Today's Blessing Came In The Form Of:

WHAT I WILL RECEIVE

Date:

What I Want God To Know:

What Makes Me So Special:

I Am Grateful For:

I Know I Will Receive:

Mood:

Today I Am Free And Open To Accept:

I Am Worthy Of:

Today I Made Room To Receive Love By:

Today I Am At A Place Where I:

Today's Blessing Came In The Form Of:

WHAT I WILL RECEIVE

Date:

What I Want God To Know:

What Makes Me So Special:

I Am Grateful For:

I Know I Will Receive:

Mood:

Today I Am Free And Open To Accept:

I Am Worthy Of:

Today I Made Room To Receive Love By:

Today I Am At A Place Where I:

Today's Blessing Came In The Form Of:

WHAT I WILL RECEIVE

Date:

What I Want God To Know:

What Makes Me So Special:

I Am Grateful For:

I Know I Will Receive:

Mood:

Today I Am Free And Open To Accept:

I Am Worthy Of:

Today I Made Room To Receive Love By:

Today I Am At A Place Where I:

Today's Blessing Came In The Form Of:

WHAT I WILL RECEIVE

Date:

Mood:

What I Want God To Know:

Today I Am Free And Open To Accept:

What Makes Me So Special:

I Am Worthy Of:

I Am Grateful For:

Today I Made Room To Receive Love By:

I Know I Will Receive:

Today I Am At A Place Where I:

Today's Blessing Came In The Form Of:

MY FIVE FAVORITE BIBLICAL SCRIPTURES ARE:

1.

2.

3.

4.

5.

NO LONGER ALLOWING WHAT IS

BAD

TO RUIN WHAT IS GOING

GOOD NOW

WHAT I WILL RECEIVE

Date:

What I Want God To Know:

What Makes Me So Special:

I Am Grateful For:

I Know I Will Receive:

Mood:

Today I Am Free And Open To Accept:

I Am Worthy Of:

Today I Made Room To Receive Love By:

Today I Am At A Place Where I:

Today's Blessing Came In The Form Of:

WHAT I WILL RECEIVE

Date:

What I Want God To Know:

What Makes Me So Special:

I Am Grateful For:

I Know I Will Receive:

Mood:

Today I Am Free And Open To Accept:

I Am Worthy Of:

Today I Made Room To Receive Love By:

Today I Am At A Place Where I:

Today's Blessing Came In The Form Of:

WHAT I WILL RECEIVE

Date:

What I Want God To Know:

What Makes Me So Special:

I Am Grateful For:

I Know I Will Receive:

Mood:

Today I Am Free And Open To Accept:

I Am Worthy Of:

Today I Made Room To Receive Love By:

Today I Am At A Place Where I:

Today's Blessing Came In The Form Of:

WHAT I WILL RECEIVE

Date: Mood:

What I Want God To Know: Today I Am Free And Open To Accept:

What Makes Me So Special: I Am Worthy Of:

I Am Grateful For: Today I Made Room To Receive Love By:

I Know I Will Receive: Today I Am At A Place Where I:

                                               Today's Blessing Came In The Form Of:

WHAT I WILL RECEIVE

Date:

What I Want God To Know:

What Makes Me So Special:

I Am Grateful For:

I Know I Will Receive:

Mood:

Today I Am Free And Open To Accept:

I Am Worthy Of:

Today I Made Room To Receive Love By:

Today I Am At A Place Where I:

Today's Blessing Came In The Form Of:

WHAT I WILL RECEIVE

Date: Mood:

What I Want God To Know: Today I Am Free And Open To Accept:

What Makes Me So Special: I Am Worthy Of:

I Am Grateful For: Today I Made Room To Receive Love By:

I Know I Will Receive: Today I Am At A Place Where I:

                                           Today's Blessing Came In The Form Of:

WHAT I WILL RECEIVE

Date: Mood:

What I Want God To Know: Today I Am Free And Open To Accept:

What Makes Me So Special: I Am Worthy Of:

I Am Grateful For: Today I Made Room To Receive Love By:

I Know I Will Receive: Today I Am At A Place Where I:

                                         Today's Blessing Came In The Form Of:

I WILL ACCEPT THEIR LOVE **BECAUSE** I AM ALREADY IN LOVE WITH **MYSELF.**

WHAT I WILL RECEIVE

Date:

What I Want God To Know:

What Makes Me So Special:

I Am Grateful For:

I Know I Will Receive:

Mood:

Today I Am Free And Open To Accept:

I Am Worthy Of:

Today I Made Room To Receive Love By:

Today I Am At A Place Where I:

Today's Blessing Came In The Form Of:

WHAT I WILL RECEIVE

Date:

What I Want God To Know:

What Makes Me So Special:

I Am Grateful For:

I Know I Will Receive:

Mood:

Today I Am Free And Open To Accept:

I Am Worthy Of:

Today I Made Room To Receive Love By:

Today I Am At A Place Where I:

Today's Blessing Came In The Form Of:

WHAT I WILL RECEIVE

Date:

What I Want God To Know:

What Makes Me So Special:

I Am Grateful For:

I Know I Will Receive:

Mood:

Today I Am Free And Open To Accept:

I Am Worthy Of:

Today I Made Room To Receive Love By:

Today I Am At A Place Where I:

Today's Blessing Came In The Form Of:

WHAT I WILL RECEIVE

Date:

What I Want God To Know:

What Makes Me So Special:

I Am Grateful For:

I Know I Will Receive:

Mood:

Today I Am Free And Open To Accept:

I Am Worthy Of:

Today I Made Room To Receive Love By:

Today I Am At A Place Where I:

Today's Blessing Came In The Form Of:

WHAT I WILL RECEIVE

Date:

What I Want God To Know:

What Makes Me So Special:

I Am Grateful For:

I Know I Will Receive:

Mood:

Today I Am Free And Open To Accept:

I Am Worthy Of:

Today I Made Room To Receive Love By:

Today I Am At A Place Where I:

Today's Blessing Came In The Form Of:

WHAT I WILL RECEIVE

Date:

What I Want God To Know:

What Makes Me So Special:

I Am Grateful For:

I Know I Will Receive:

Mood:

Today I Am Free And Open To Accept:

I Am Worthy Of:

Today I Made Room To Receive Love By:

Today I Am At A Place Where I:

Today's Blessing Came In The Form Of:

I HAVE IT BECAUSE I BELIEVE IT
BELONGS TO ME.
— LOVE

WHAT I WILL RECEIVE

Date:

What I Want God To Know:

What Makes Me So Special:

I Am Grateful For:

I Know I Will Receive:

Mood:

Today I Am Free And Open To Accept:

I Am Worthy Of:

Today I Made Room To Receive Love By:

Today I Am At A Place Where I:

Today's Blessing Came In The Form Of:

WHAT I WILL RECEIVE

Date: Mood:

What I Want God To Know: Today I Am Free And Open To Accept:

What Makes Me So Special: I Am Worthy Of:

I Am Grateful For: Today I Made Room To Receive Love By:

I Know I Will Receive: Today I Am At A Place Where I:

                                         Today's Blessing Came In The Form Of:

I BELIEVED IN SOMETHING

NEW

AND SO I GOT IT.

Made in the USA
Middletown, DE
16 June 2022

67216507R00130